This Christmas Planner belongs to

_____

*It's the
most
wonderful time
of the year*

About This Planner

This Planner has been created to help you stay organized in the run up to the holiday season.

It's divided into easy sections, making it easy for you to stay organized in the run up to and right through the holiday season.

You'll discover:

- ✓ Your Holiday Bucket List
- ✓ Your Christmas Wish List
- ✓ Calendar for November & December
- ✓ Christmas & New Year Countdown checklist
- ✓ Holiday Budget planner
- ✓ Holiday Gift List, with extra space for top priority gifts
- ✓ Online Order Tracker
- ✓ Stocking Stuffers
- ✓ Christmas Cards list
- ✓ Menu Planner
- ✓ Shopping Checklist
- ✓ Holiday Recipes
- ✓ Favorite Memories
- ✓ Notes for next year

You'll find everything you'll need to keep you organized. If you love lists, you'll love this Christmas planner!

Holiday Bucket List

PLACES TO GO	PEOPLE TO SEE

PLACES TO GO	PEOPLE TO SEE

TRADITIONS	HOUSE & HOME

THINGS TO MAKE	THINGS TO BAKE

Holiday Bucket List

MOVIES TO WATCH	TV TO WATCH

OUT & ABOUT	FESTIVE FOOD

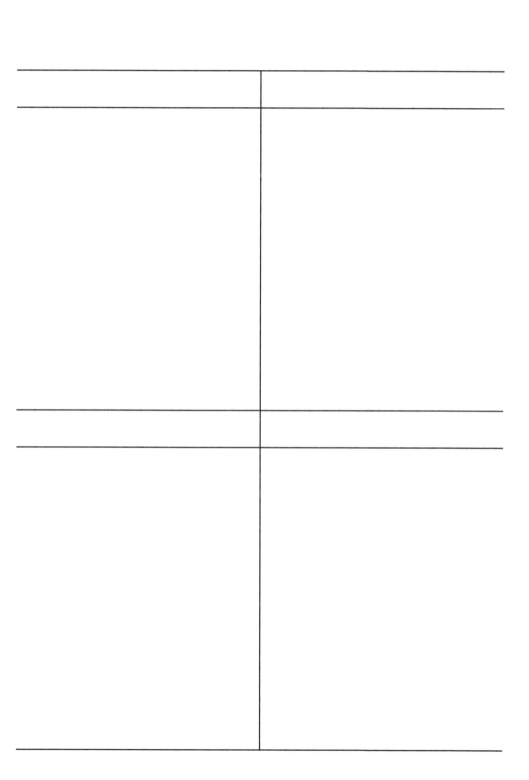

Holiday Bucket List

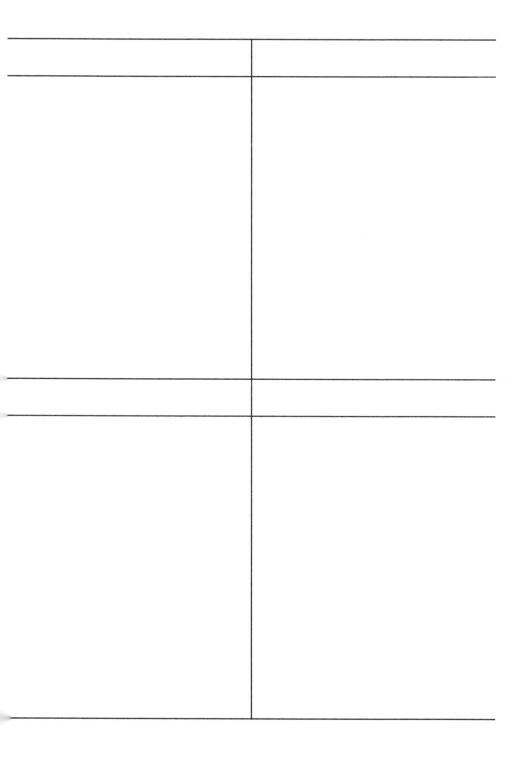

My Christmas Wish List

ITEM	SHOP

ITEM	SHOP

My Christmas Wish List

ITEM	SHOP

ITEM	SHOP

November

TO DO	MON	TUES	WEDS

THUR	FRI	SAT	SUN

December

TO DO	MON	TUES	WEDS

THUR	FRI	SAT	SUN

Christmas Countdown Checklist

1st December	2nd December

3rd December	4th December

5th December	6th December

7th December	8th December

Christmas Countdown Checklist

9ᵗʰ December	10ᵗʰ December

11ᵗʰ December	12ᵗʰ December

13th December	14th December

15th December	16th December

Christmas Countdown Checklist

17th December	18th December

19th December	20th December

21st December	22nd December

23rd December	Notes

Christmas Eve Checklist

Christmas Eve - 24th December

Christmas Day Checklist

Boxing Day Checklist

Boxing Day - 26th December

27th December	28th December

29th December	30th December

New Year Countdown Checklist

New Year's Eve - 31st December

_____

_____

_____

_____

_____

_____

_____

_____

New Year's Day - 1st January

_____

_____

_____

_____

_____

_____

_____

Notes

Holiday Budget Planner

ITEM	BUDGET	ACTUAL
TOTAL		

ITEM	BUDGET	ACTUAL
TOTAL		

Holiday Budget Planner

ITEM	BUDGET	ACTUAL
TOTAL		

ITEM	BUDGET	ACTUAL
TOTAL		

Holiday Budget Planner

ITEM	BUDGET	ACTUAL
TOTAL		

ITEM	BUDGET	ACTUAL
TOTAL		

Holiday Budget Planner

ITEM	BUDGET	ACTUAL
TOTAL		

ITEM	BUDGET	ACTUAL
TOTAL		

Top Priority

Gift for: _____

GIFT	SHOP	PRICE	Ordered	Received	Wrapped
			◯	◯	◯
			◯	◯	◯
			◯	◯	◯
			◯	◯	◯
			◯	◯	◯
			◯	◯	◯
			◯	◯	◯
			◯	◯	◯
			◯	◯	◯
			◯	◯	◯
			◯	◯	◯
			◯	◯	◯
			◯	◯	◯
			◯	◯	◯
			◯	◯	◯
			◯	◯	◯
			◯	◯	◯
			◯	◯	◯

Gift for:

GIFT	SHOP	PRICE	Ordered	Received	Wrapped
			◯	◯	◯
			◯	◯	◯
			◯	◯	◯
			◯	◯	◯
			◯	◯	◯
			◯	◯	◯
			◯	◯	◯
			◯	◯	◯
			◯	◯	◯
			◯	◯	◯
			◯	◯	◯
			◯	◯	◯
			◯	◯	◯
			◯	◯	◯
			◯	◯	◯
			◯	◯	◯
			◯	◯	◯
			◯	◯	◯

Top Priority

Gift for: ....

GIFT	SHOP	PRICE	Ordered	Received	Wrapped
			○	○	○
			○	○	○
			○	○	○
			○	○	○
			○	○	○
			○	○	○
			○	○	○
			○	○	○
			○	○	○
			○	○	○
			○	○	○
			○	○	○
			○	○	○
			○	○	○
			○	○	○
			○	○	○
			○	○	○
			○	○	○

Gift for:

_____

GIFT	SHOP	PRICE	Ordered	Received	Wrapped
			○	○	○
			○	○	○
			○	○	○
			○	○	○
			○	○	○
			○	○	○
			○	○	○
			○	○	○
			○	○	○
			○	○	○
			○	○	○
			○	○	○
			○	○	○
			○	○	○
			○	○	○
			○	○	○
			○	○	○
			○	○	○

Top Priority

Gift for:

GIFT	SHOP	PRICE	Ordered	Received	Wrapped
			○	○	○
			○	○	○
			○	○	○
			○	○	○
			○	○	○
			○	○	○
			○	○	○
			○	○	○
			○	○	○
			○	○	○
			○	○	○
			○	○	○
			○	○	○
			○	○	○
			○	○	○
			○	○	○
			○	○	○
			○	○	○

Gift for:

_____

GIFT	SHOP	PRICE	Ordered	Received	Wrapped
			○	○	○
			○	○	○
			○	○	○
			○	○	○
			○	○	○
			○	○	○
			○	○	○
			○	○	○
			○	○	○
			○	○	○
			○	○	○
			○	○	○
			○	○	○
			○	○	○
			○	○	○
			○	○	○
			○	○	○
			○	○	○

Top Priority

Gift for:
....

GIFT	SHOP	PRICE	Ordered	Received	Wrapped
			◯	◯	◯
			◯	◯	◯
			◯	◯	◯
			◯	◯	◯
			◯	◯	◯
			◯	◯	◯
			◯	◯	◯
			◯	◯	◯
			◯	◯	◯
			◯	◯	◯
			◯	◯	◯
			◯	◯	◯
			◯	◯	◯
			◯	◯	◯
			◯	◯	◯
			◯	◯	◯
			◯	◯	◯
			◯	◯	◯

Gift for:

_____

GIFT	SHOP	PRICE	Ordered	Received	Wrapped
			○	○	○
			○	○	○
			○	○	○
			○	○	○
			○	○	○
			○	○	○
			○	○	○
			○	○	○
			○	○	○
			○	○	○
			○	○	○
			○	○	○
			○	○	○
			○	○	○
			○	○	○
			○	○	○
			○	○	○
			○	○	○

Top Priority

Gift for:
....

GIFT	SHOP	PRICE	Ordered	Received	Wrapped
			○	○	○
			○	○	○
			○	○	○
			○	○	○
			○	○	○
			○	○	○
			○	○	○
			○	○	○
			○	○	○
			○	○	○
			○	○	○
			○	○	○
			○	○	○
			○	○	○
			○	○	○
			○	○	○
			○	○	○
			○	○	○

Gift for:

_____

GIFT	SHOP	PRICE	Ordered	Received	Wrapped
			◯	◯	◯
			◯	◯	◯
			◯	◯	◯
			◯	◯	◯
			◯	◯	◯
			◯	◯	◯
			◯	◯	◯
			◯	◯	◯
			◯	◯	◯
			◯	◯	◯
			◯	◯	◯
			◯	◯	◯
			◯	◯	◯
			◯	◯	◯
			◯	◯	◯
			◯	◯	◯
			◯	◯	◯
			◯	◯	◯

Top Priority

Gift for:

GIFT	SHOP	PRICE	Ordered	Received	Wrapped
			◯	◯	◯
			◯	◯	◯
			◯	◯	◯
			◯	◯	◯
			◯	◯	◯
			◯	◯	◯
			◯	◯	◯
			◯	◯	◯
			◯	◯	◯
			◯	◯	◯
			◯	◯	◯
			◯	◯	◯
			◯	◯	◯
			◯	◯	◯
			◯	◯	◯
			◯	◯	◯
			◯	◯	◯
			◯	◯	◯

Gift for:

_____

GIFT	SHOP	PRICE	Ordered	Received	Wrapped
			◯	◯	◯
			◯	◯	◯
			◯	◯	◯
			◯	◯	◯
			◯	◯	◯
			◯	◯	◯
			◯	◯	◯
			◯	◯	◯
			◯	◯	◯
			◯	◯	◯
			◯	◯	◯
			◯	◯	◯
			◯	◯	◯
			◯	◯	◯
			◯	◯	◯
			◯	◯	◯
			◯	◯	◯
			◯	◯	◯

Holiday Gift List

NAME:

NAME:

NAME:

NAME:

NAME:	NAME:

NAME:	NAME:

Holiday Gift List

NAME:

NAME:

NAME:

NAME:

NAME:

NAME:

NAME:

NAME:

Holiday Gift List

NAME:

NAME:

NAME:

NAME:

NAME:	NAME:
NAME:	NAME:

Holiday Gift List

NAME:	NAME:
NAME:	**NAME:**

NAME:

NAME:

NAME:

NAME:

Holiday Gift List

NAME:	NAME:
NAME:	**NAME:**

NAME:	NAME:
NAME:	**NAME:**

Holiday Gift List

NAME:	NAME:

NAME:	NAME:

NAME:	NAME:
NAME:	NAME:

Holiday Gift List

NAME:	NAME:
NAME:	NAME:
NAME:	NAME:
NAME:	NAME:

NAME:	NAME:
NAME:	NAME:
NAME:	NAME:
NAME:	NAME:

Holiday Gift List

NAME:	NAME:
NAME:	NAME:
NAME:	NAME:
NAME:	NAME:

NAME:	NAME:
NAME:	NAME:
NAME:	NAME:
NAME:	NAME:

Online Order Tracker

GIFT	PRICE	SHOP	Ordered	Received	Wrapped
			○	○	○
			○	○	○
			○	○	○
			○	○	○
			○	○	○
			○	○	○
			○	○	○
			○	○	○
			○	○	○
			○	○	○
			○	○	○
			○	○	○
			○	○	○
			○	○	○
			○	○	○
			○	○	○
			○	○	○
			○	○	○

GIFT	PRICE	SHOP	Ordered	Received	Wrapped
			◯	◯	◯
			◯	◯	◯
			◯	◯	◯
			◯	◯	◯
			◯	◯	◯
			◯	◯	◯
			◯	◯	◯
			◯	◯	◯
			◯	◯	◯
			◯	◯	◯
			◯	◯	◯
			◯	◯	◯
			◯	◯	◯
			◯	◯	◯
			◯	◯	◯
			◯	◯	◯
			◯	◯	◯
			◯	◯	◯

Online Order Tracker

GIFT	PRICE	SHOP	Ordered	Received	Wrapped
			○	○	○
			○	○	○
			○	○	○
			○	○	○
			○	○	○
			○	○	○
			○	○	○
			○	○	○
			○	○	○
			○	○	○
			○	○	○
			○	○	○
			○	○	○
			○	○	○
			○	○	○
			○	○	○
			○	○	○
			○	○	○

GIFT	PRICE	SHOP	Ordered	Received	Wrapped
			○	○	○
			○	○	○
			○	○	○
			○	○	○
			○	○	○
			○	○	○
			○	○	○
			○	○	○
			○	○	○
			○	○	○
			○	○	○
			○	○	○
			○	○	○
			○	○	○
			○	○	○
			○	○	○
			○	○	○
			○	○	○

Online Order Tracker

GIFT	PRICE	SHOP	Ordered	Received	Wrapped
			○	○	○
			○	○	○
			○	○	○
			○	○	○
			○	○	○
			○	○	○
			○	○	○
			○	○	○
			○	○	○
			○	○	○
			○	○	○
			○	○	○
			○	○	○
			○	○	○
			○	○	○
			○	○	○
			○	○	○
			○	○	○

GIFT	PRICE	SHOP	Ordered	Received	Wrapped
			○	○	○
			○	○	○
			○	○	○
			○	○	○
			○	○	○
			○	○	○
			○	○	○
			○	○	○
			○	○	○
			○	○	○
			○	○	○
			○	○	○
			○	○	○
			○	○	○
			○	○	○
			○	○	○
			○	○	○
			○	○	○

Online Order Tracker

GIFT	PRICE	SHOP	Ordered	Received	Wrapped
			○	○	○
			○	○	○
			○	○	○
			○	○	○
			○	○	○
			○	○	○
			○	○	○
			○	○	○
			○	○	○
			○	○	○
			○	○	○
			○	○	○
			○	○	○
			○	○	○
			○	○	○
			○	○	○
			○	○	○
			○	○	○

GIFT	PRICE	SHOP	Ordered	Received	Wrapped
			○	○	○
			○	○	○
			○	○	○
			○	○	○
			○	○	○
			○	○	○
			○	○	○
			○	○	○
			○	○	○
			○	○	○
			○	○	○
			○	○	○
			○	○	○
			○	○	○
			○	○	○
			○	○	○
			○	○	○
			○	○	○

Online Order Tracker

GIFT	PRICE	SHOP	Ordered	Received	Wrapped
			◯	◯	◯
			◯	◯	◯
			◯	◯	◯
			◯	◯	◯
			◯	◯	◯
			◯	◯	◯
			◯	◯	◯
			◯	◯	◯
			◯	◯	◯
			◯	◯	◯
			◯	◯	◯
			◯	◯	◯
			◯	◯	◯
			◯	◯	◯
			◯	◯	◯
			◯	◯	◯
			◯	◯	◯
			◯	◯	◯

GIFT	PRICE	SHOP	Ordered	Received	Wrapped
			○	○	○
			○	○	○
			○	○	○
			○	○	○
			○	○	○
			○	○	○
			○	○	○
			○	○	○
			○	○	○
			○	○	○
			○	○	○
			○	○	○
			○	○	○
			○	○	○
			○	○	○
			○	○	○
			○	○	○
			○	○	○

Online Order Tracker

GIFT	PRICE	SHOP	Ordered	Received	Wrapped
			○	○	○
			○	○	○
			○	○	○
			○	○	○
			○	○	○
			○	○	○
			○	○	○
			○	○	○
			○	○	○
			○	○	○
			○	○	○
			○	○	○
			○	○	○
			○	○	○
			○	○	○
			○	○	○
			○	○	○
			○	○	○

GIFT	PRICE	SHOP	Ordered	Received	Wrapped
			◯	◯	◯
			◯	◯	◯
			◯	◯	◯
			◯	◯	◯
			◯	◯	◯
			◯	◯	◯
			◯	◯	◯
			◯	◯	◯
			◯	◯	◯
			◯	◯	◯
			◯	◯	◯
			◯	◯	◯
			◯	◯	◯
			◯	◯	◯
			◯	◯	◯
			◯	◯	◯
			◯	◯	◯
			◯	◯	◯

Stocking Stuffers

For:

GIFT	SHOP	PRICE	Ordered	Received
			○	○
			○	○
			○	○
			○	○
			○	○
			○	○
			○	○
			○	○
			○	○
			○	○
			○	○
			○	○
			○	○
			○	○
			○	○
			○	○
			○	○
			○	○

For:

GIFT	SHOP	PRICE	Ordered	Received
			○	○
			○	○
			○	○
			○	○
			○	○
			○	○
			○	○
			○	○
			○	○
			○	○
			○	○
			○	○
			○	○
			○	○
			○	○
			○	○
			○	○
			○	○
			○	○

Stocking Stuffers

For: ....

GIFT	SHOP	PRICE	Ordered	Received
			◯	◯
			◯	◯
			◯	◯
			◯	◯
			◯	◯
			◯	◯
			◯	◯
			◯	◯
			◯	◯
			◯	◯
			◯	◯
			◯	◯
			◯	◯
			◯	◯
			◯	◯
			◯	◯
			◯	◯
			◯	◯
			◯	◯

For:

GIFT	SHOP	PRICE	Ordered	Received
			◯	◯
			◯	◯
			◯	◯
			◯	◯
			◯	◯
			◯	◯
			◯	◯
			◯	◯
			◯	◯
			◯	◯
			◯	◯
			◯	◯
			◯	◯
			◯	◯
			◯	◯
			◯	◯
			◯	◯
			◯	◯
			◯	◯

Stocking Stuffers

For: ....

GIFT	SHOP	PRICE	Ordered	Received
			○	○
			○	○
			○	○
			○	○
			○	○
			○	○
			○	○
			○	○
			○	○
			○	○
			○	○
			○	○
			○	○
			○	○
			○	○
			○	○
			○	○
			○	○
			○	○

For:
....

GIFT	SHOP	PRICE	Ordered	Received
			◯	◯
			◯	◯
			◯	◯
			◯	◯
			◯	◯
			◯	◯
			◯	◯
			◯	◯
			◯	◯
			◯	◯
			◯	◯
			◯	◯
			◯	◯
			◯	◯
			◯	◯
			◯	◯
			◯	◯
			◯	◯

Stocking Stuffers

For:

GIFT	SHOP	PRICE	Ordered	Received
			◯	◯
			◯	◯
			◯	◯
			◯	◯
			◯	◯
			◯	◯
			◯	◯
			◯	◯
			◯	◯
			◯	◯
			◯	◯
			◯	◯
			◯	◯
			◯	◯
			◯	◯
			◯	◯
			◯	◯
			◯	◯

For:

GIFT	SHOP	PRICE	Ordered	Received
			◯	◯
			◯	◯
			◯	◯
			◯	◯
			◯	◯
			◯	◯
			◯	◯
			◯	◯
			◯	◯
			◯	◯
			◯	◯
			◯	◯
			◯	◯
			◯	◯
			◯	◯
			◯	◯
			◯	◯
			◯	◯
			◯	◯

Christmas Card List

NAME & ADDRESS

	SENT	REC'D
	◯	◯

	SENT	REC'D
	◯	◯

	SENT	REC'D
	◯	◯

	SENT	REC'D
	◯	◯

	SENT	REC'D
	◯	◯

NAME & ADDRESS

	SENT	REC'D
	◯	◯
	SENT	REC'D
	◯	◯
	SENT	REC'D
	◯	◯
	SENT	REC'D
	◯	◯
	SENT	REC'D
	◯	◯

Christmas Card List

NAME & ADDRESS

	SENT	REC'D
	○	○

	SENT	REC'D
	○	○

	SENT	REC'D
	○	○

	SENT	REC'D
	○	○

	SENT	REC'D
	○	○

NAME & ADDRESS

	SENT	REC'D
	◯	◯

	SENT	REC'D
	◯	◯

	SENT	REC'D
	◯	◯

	SENT	REC'D
	◯	◯

	SENT	REC'D
	◯	◯

Christmas Card List

NAME & ADDRESS

	SENT	REC'D
	◯	◯

	SENT	REC'D
	◯	◯

	SENT	REC'D
	◯	◯

	SENT	REC'D
	◯	◯

	SENT	REC'D
	◯	◯

NAME & ADDRESS

	SENT	REC'D
	◯	◯

	SENT	REC'D
	◯	◯

	SENT	REC'D
	◯	◯

	SENT	REC'D
	◯	◯

	SENT	REC'D
	◯	◯

Christmas Card List

NAME & ADDRESS

	SENT	REC'D
	◯	◯

	SENT	REC'D
	◯	◯

	SENT	REC'D
	◯	◯

	SENT	REC'D
	◯	◯

	SENT	REC'D
	◯	◯

NAME & ADDRESS

	SENT	REC'D
	◯	◯

	SENT	REC'D
	◯	◯

	SENT	REC'D
	◯	◯

	SENT	REC'D
	◯	◯

	SENT	REC'D
	◯	◯

Christmas Card List

NAME & ADDRESS

	SENT	REC'D
	◯	◯

	SENT	REC'D
	◯	◯

	SENT	REC'D
	◯	◯

	SENT	REC'D
	◯	◯

	SENT	REC'D
	◯	◯

NAME & ADDRESS

	SENT	REC'D
	○	○

	SENT	REC'D
	○	○

	SENT	REC'D
	○	○

	SENT	REC'D
	○	○

	SENT	REC'D
	○	○

Christmas Card List

NAME & ADDRESS

	SENT	REC'D
	◯	◯

	SENT	REC'D
	◯	◯

	SENT	REC'D
	◯	◯

	SENT	REC'D
	◯	◯

	SENT	REC'D
	◯	◯

NAME & ADDRESS

	SENT	REC'D
	◯	◯

	SENT	REC'D
	◯	◯

	SENT	REC'D
	◯	◯

	SENT	REC'D
	◯	◯

	SENT	REC'D
	◯	◯

Christmas Card List

NAME & ADDRESS

	SENT	REC'D
	◯	◯

	SENT	REC'D
	◯	◯

	SENT	REC'D
	◯	◯

	SENT	REC'D
	◯	◯

	SENT	REC'D
	◯	◯

NAME & ADDRESS

	SENT	REC'D
	◯	◯

	SENT	REC'D
	◯	◯

	SENT	REC'D
	◯	◯

	SENT	REC'D
	◯	◯

	SENT	REC'D
	◯	◯

Christmas Card List

NAME & ADDRESS

	SENT	REC'D
	◯	◯

	SENT	REC'D
	◯	◯

	SENT	REC'D
	◯	◯

	SENT	REC'D
	◯	◯

	SENT	REC'D
	◯	◯

NAME & ADDRESS

	SENT	REC'D
	◯	◯

	SENT	REC'D
	◯	◯

	SENT	REC'D
	◯	◯

	SENT	REC'D
	◯	◯

	SENT	REC'D
	◯	◯

Christmas Card List

NAME & ADDRESS

	SENT	REC'D
	◯	◯

	SENT	REC'D
	◯	◯

	SENT	REC'D
	◯	◯

	SENT	REC'D
	◯	◯

	SENT	REC'D
	◯	◯

NAME & ADDRESS

	SENT	REC'D
	◯	◯

	SENT	REC'D
	◯	◯

	SENT	REC'D
	◯	◯

	SENT	REC'D
	◯	◯

	SENT	REC'D
	◯	◯

Christmas Card List

NAME & ADDRESS

	SENT	REC'D
	◯	◯

	SENT	REC'D
	◯	◯

	SENT	REC'D
	◯	◯

	SENT	REC'D
	◯	◯

	SENT	REC'D
	◯	◯

NAME & ADDRESS

	SENT	REC'D
	○	○

	SENT	REC'D
	○	○

	SENT	REC'D
	○	○

	SENT	REC'D
	○	○

	SENT	REC'D
	○	○

Christmas Card List

NAME & ADDRESS

	SENT	REC'D
	○	○

	SENT	REC'D
	○	○

	SENT	REC'D
	○	○

	SENT	REC'D
	○	○

	SENT	REC'D
	○	○

NAME & ADDRESS

	SENT	REC'D
	◯	◯

	SENT	REC'D
	◯	◯

	SENT	REC'D
	◯	◯

	SENT	REC'D
	◯	◯

	SENT	REC'D
	◯	◯

Menu Planner

Day:

BREAKFAST	SNACKS

LUNCH

STARTERS	MAIN	DESSERT
		DRINKS

DINNER

STARTERS	MAIN	DESSERT
		DRINKS

Day:

BREAKFAST	SNACKS

LUNCH

STARTERS	MAIN	DESSERT
		DRINKS

DINNER

STARTERS	MAIN	DESSERT
		DRINKS

Menu Planner

Day:

BREAKFAST

SNACKS

LUNCH

STARTERS

MAIN

DESSERT

DRINKS

DINNER

STARTERS

MAIN

DESSERT

DRINKS

Day:

BREAKFAST	SNACKS

LUNCH

STARTERS	MAIN	DESSERT
		DRINKS

DINNER

STARTERS	MAIN	DESSERT
		DRINKS

Menu Planner

Day:

BREAKFAST	SNACKS

LUNCH

STARTERS	MAIN	DESSERT
		DRINKS

DINNER

STARTERS	MAIN	DESSERT
		DRINKS

Day:

BREAKFAST	SNACKS

LUNCH

STARTERS	MAIN	DESSERT
		DRINKS

DINNER

STARTERS	MAIN	DESSERT
		DRINKS

Shopping Checklist

ITEM		ITEM	
	○		○
	○		○
	○		○
	○		○
	○		○
	○		○
	○		○
	○		○
	○		○
	○		○
	○		○
	○		○
	○		○
	○		○
	○		○
	○		○
	○		○
	○		○
	○		○
	○		○

ITEM		ITEM	
	○		○
	○		○
	○		○
	○		○
	○		○
	○		○
	○		○
	○		○
	○		○
	○		○
	○		○
	○		○
	○		○
	○		○
	○		○
	○		○
	○		○
	○		○
	○		○
	○		○

Shopping Checklist

ITEM		ITEM	
	○		○
	○		○
	○		○
	○		○
	○		○
	○		○
	○		○
	○		○
	○		○
	○		○
	○		○
	○		○
	○		○
	○		○
	○		○
	○		○
	○		○
	○		○
	○		○

ITEM		ITEM	
	○		○
	○		○
	○		○
	○		○
	○		○
	○		○
	○		○
	○		○
	○		○
	○		○
	○		○
	○		○
	○		○
	○		○
	○		○
	○		○
	○		○
	○		○
	○		○
	○		○

Shopping Checklist

ITEM		ITEM	
	◯		◯
	◯		◯
	◯		◯
	◯		◯
	◯		◯
	◯		◯
	◯		◯
	◯		◯
	◯		◯
	◯		◯
	◯		◯
	◯		◯
	◯		◯
	◯		◯
	◯		◯
	◯		◯
	◯		◯
	◯		◯
	◯		◯

ITEM		ITEM	
	◯		◯
	◯		◯
	◯		◯
	◯		◯
	◯		◯
	◯		◯
	◯		◯
	◯		◯
	◯		◯
	◯		◯
	◯		◯
	◯		◯
	◯		◯
	◯		◯
	◯		◯
	◯		◯
	◯		◯
	◯		◯
	◯		◯
	◯		◯

Shopping Checklist

ITEM		ITEM	
	○		○
	○		○
	○		○
	○		○
	○		○
	○		○
	○		○
	○		○
	○		○
	○		○
	○		○
	○		○
	○		○
	○		○
	○		○
	○		○
	○		○
	○		○
	○		○
	○		○

ITEM		ITEM	
	○		○
	○		○
	○		○
	○		○
	○		○
	○		○
	○		○
	○		○
	○		○
	○		○
	○		○
	○		○
	○		○
	○		○
	○		○
	○		○
	○		○
	○		○
	○		○

Holiday Recipes

INGREDIENTS

METHOD

INGREDIENTS

METHOD

Holiday Recipes

INGREDIENTS	

METHOD

INGREDIENTS

METHOD

Holiday Recipes

INGREDIENTS	

METHOD

INGREDIENTS

METHOD

Holiday Recipes

INGREDIENTS

METHOD

INGREDIENTS

METHOD

Holiday Recipes

INGREDIENTS

METHOD

INGREDIENTS

METHOD

Holiday Recipes

INGREDIENTS	

METHOD

INGREDIENTS

METHOD

Holiday Recipes

INGREDIENTS

METHOD

INGREDIENTS

METHOD

Favorite Holiday Memories

PEOPLE WE SAW

PLACES WE WENT

FOOD WE ATE	FUN

FUN TIMES WE HAD

Favorite Holiday Memories

TRADITIONS

OUT & ABOUT / EVENTS

THINGS I MADE	THINGS I BAKED

MOVIES & TV

Favorite Holiday Memories

HOUSE & HOME	

Notes for Next Year

Notes for Next Year

Notes for Next Year

Made in the USA
Monee, IL
15 November 2024

70202331R00085